"Self-care is how you take your power back."

~ Lalah Delia

Praise for Self Care Sh*t
The Workbook

"The only way for me to be my best team player is to know what I need to shine. For so long I was always wondering what I could do to help others be their best and it took a toll on me. Self-care is an ever-evolving journey, and Kathy Leckey provides a look at how to narrow the focus to what YOU need to be your best self so you can ENJOY all the moments the we need to fulfill ME and WE."

~ Brandi Chastain, 2x Olympic Gold Medalist, 2x World Cup Champion, National Soccer Hall of Fame

"Self-care is so important to showing up as the best version of yourself. Kathy has created a unique workbook that you'll refer back to constantly."

~ Heather Monahan, 2x Bestselling Author, Top 50 Keynote Speaker, Top 100 Podcast: "Creating Confidence", CEO

"Kathy is a friend and colleague I've known for years. Her understanding of people struggling with codependency shines through in everything she does, from speaking engagements to workshops. Kathy has this captivating way about her that never fails to make an audience feel seen-heard and understood! I am confident that her journal will allow for you to feel the same."

~ Matthew Pfifer MSEd, Founder of Toxic to Triumph Author, Podcast host, Speaker

"Kathy authors this personal guide with the fierceness of a "momma bear" and gentleness of a nudge to do our best. My Self Care Sh*t guides us coming and going...in the best ways possible."

~ Stacy Feiner, PsyD, Innovative Psychiatrist, CEO of Feiner Enterprises.

"So many people talk about reaching contentment but don't know where to start. This book is a wonderfully structured road map and guide to help us get to know what makes us feel good. It also helps us identify what actions we can take every day to build a life of self-care and fulfillment that is unique to each of us. I will definitely be using this book in my practice."

~ Nancy C. Lucas, MS, LCSW

"This workbook is thought-provoking. It welcomes others to their own journey who will benefit from your observations, insights, and emphasis on goal setting guided by values. "

~ Thomas Unger, PhD
Clinical Psychologist, Buffalo, New York

MY
SELF
CARE
SH*T

Kathy Leckey

This book is dedicated
to the woman I found
on these pages(me)
and to everyone &
every experience
that has shaped me.

contents

contents

INTRODUCTION

We hear the phrase self-care all of the time, especially when it comes to advice from friends and family when we are going through a crisis. Well-meaning people routinely tell us to take care of ourselves, but if we are struggling with codependency, as so many of us are, we may not even know what that means.

Simply put self-care is about knowing what makes you happy, believing you are worthy of having it, setting boundaries to make space for it, and letting go of what others may think of your choices. As we heal from codependency, we begin to understand the difference between self-care and selfishness.

In our struggle with codependency, our unhealthy beliefs and thoughts keep us focused on doing for others until we lose sight of ourselves. We know what the people around us want, need, and like, but we don't know the same things about ourselves. We may find we don't know the simplest of things about ourselves like what our favorite food or restaurant is. We pride ourselves on being easy-going or able to "go with the flow", but it may actually be that we can't make a choice because we are so used to making decisions based on other people's needs before our own. We may worry about making the "wrong" decision for the group until we heal and realize it is up to everyone to speak up for themselves. We begin to realize that we deserve to have an opinion and to ask for what we want always. It doesn't mean we always get what we want, but now we know what we want and aren't afraid to give our opinion anymore.

As we heal and get reacquainted with ourselves, or connect with ourselves for the first time, we start to notice our own likes and dislikes, preferences, needs and wants. When I first started to heal from codependency, I had absolutely no idea what self-care really meant. A massage once a year? Going for a mani/pedi? Sleep until noon? I had no idea!

A single mom, working multiple jobs, with three busy teenagers, I had no time to waste on these "frivolous" activities. I could not afford these self-perceived luxuries. Most importantly, I wanted to find things that lasted longer than an hour of pampering. At a complete loss, I actually googled "how to self-care" for some ideas. That's when I ran into trouble.

Everything I found was "Take quiet time for yourself." "Fill your day with things that bring you joy!" Do what you want to do!". Sounds great! Sounds easy! But, the big problem was that I didn't know what I liked anymore. What do I love to do? What brings me joy? I had no idea. I was focused on the situation I was in and the anger about how I got there. My attention was on my kids' activities, sports, well being, etc. For the first time, I was 100% financially responsible for my family on top of everything else that landed on my shoulders. I was so focused on surviving that what I needed or wanted to thrive was not even on my radar.

It became very apparent to me how much I did not know myself when I tried to fill out my profile on dating apps. I honestly had no idea how to describe myself in 50 words or less. What are my hobbies? Driving the kids to their games, work, worrying? What is my favorite movie? When was the last time I watched a movie without falling asleep from exhaustion?

I would do anything to avoid being alone with myself. I panicked at the idea of having time alone. Instead, I distracted myself from myself by finding anything I could to stay busy, taking care of others, and staying in toxic relationships over being alone.

I started keeping a list on my phone. Whenever something made me smile or feel a moment's peace, I put it on the list. Anytime I got jealous of what someone else was doing I added it to the list. That was a sign of something I wanted for myself but didn't think I could do. I started to find things like breathing exercises that had lasting effects. Breathing is free and can be done anywhere, anytime, day or night. It was working for me so I kept adding to the lists on my phone, in my journals, and on sticky notes on my desk.

I created this book for myself to have one place to keep all of my lists and now I am ready to share it with you. This is a place to spend a few quiet minutes at a time to discover and reconnect with yourself. This book is a place for reminders of what brings you joy. Things that you know will pull you out of a bad mood. It will be where you come for a gentle reminder of the good things in your life when you are struggling.

I wish I had this book when I was younger before I had a career, responsibilities, and a family. Before I forgot who I was beyond an employee, a wife, and a mother.

This may feel overwhelming at first. It's called a workbook because it is work. Do what you can, put it down, and come back to it when you are ready. Even as I went through adding examples on each list, I realized how challenging it still is for me to answer some of these questions. Some of the examples are true for me, some are made up to give you ideas. Every person who fills this out will have their own unique answers. You are the only one who can do this work for you.

This is THE place for lists of what to do when you start to begin to create healthy boundaries and find yourself with free time to do what you love to do. I had absolutely no idea what I wanted to do with my time. Now I look forward to it I crave it, even choose it. One of my proudest moments of healing was when I was asked to go out with a friend and said no because I wanted to stay home and do some of the things I love to do. Enjoy getting to know you, enjoying your own company, and what it means to truly take care of yourself.

Take care of yourself,
Kathy

"You yourself, as much as anybody in the entire universe, deserve your love and affection."

~Buddha

FOREWARD

I've known Kathy Leckey and her family for over two decades most of that from a distance as acquaintances. Distance has a way of being a filter. You see a glimpse of someone's life and character and form opinions but you're not seeing the full picture. Over the last 5 years, that has changed as I've had a front row set to Kathy's life, unfiltered and raw.

My initial impressions were of a supportive wife to a former high school football teammate of mine and a devoted and involved mother to three beautiful and talented children. One thing I always knew was that Kathy cared about other people and was active and passionate about giving back to her community.

As Kathy and I became work colleagues and friends I realized that those things were all true, in fact they were even more predominant than I had imagined. She wasn't playing a character. What made that inspiring was when I came to realize the significant adversity that Kathy has faced in her life. Seeing things up close and personal and being privy to the good, the bad and the ugly I very quickly realized that Kathy's selfless heart was even more remarkable than I had thought. It's easy to be benevolent when things are going well but often that waivers as people get smacked in the face by adversity. Kathy has never wavered. She is strong, she is resilient and she is selfless. Kathy's ability to consistently get knocked down only to dust herself off is astounding so when she embarked on a coaching career to help others overcome co-dependency and learn self-care I knew the results would be profound.

In this workbook, you will see the framework she teaches for self-care. It's extremely user-friendly, practical, and fun. The magic is Kathy doesn't give you all the answers on a silver platter, instead, she acts as a gentle guide to help people discover the answers on their own. Kathy is a natural teacher and she doesn't do it from an ivory tower. She does it by unashamedly pulling from her own life experiences. She walks the talk and then some. I'm excited about the impact that this book will have on people's lives.

This is not a one-and-done book of exercises to do and then forget about. This book is something you'll refer back to over and over as your life evolves and as you learn the critical tools of self-care.

I'm proud of Kathy for creating this. I'm proud of you for investing in it. I wish you luck on your journey but I'm confident you'll reach your goals because you have an expert guide to help you along the way.

Scott MacGregor, Founder & CEO of SomethingNew LLC & Founder of the Talent Champions Council, 4x Author of the "Standing O!" Series, Record 6 consecutive American Business Awards Winner for Innovation

"Take the time today to love yourself. You deserve it."

~Avina Celeste

WHEEL OF LIFE

Directions: Focus on each area of your life and rate your satisfaction level with it (from 0-10) with 0 (not satisfied) being at the center of the wheel and 10 (extremely satisfied) being the outside of the wheel. Draw a line connecting the dots to see where your wheel is off balance. Use this wheel to focus on the areas that you have identified as not extremely satisfied.

	WHERE I AM TODAY	WHERE I WANT TO BE	WHAT'S IN THE WAY
Self-care			
Career			
Finances			
Food			
Exercise			
Family Life			
Friends			
Romantic Life			
Spirituality			
Learning			

- ☐ SONG WRITING
- ☐ DANCE
- ☐ TAKE A CLASS
- ☐ ENTERTAINING
- ☐ POETRY/CREATIVE WRITING
- ☐ PHOTOGRAPHY
- ☐ TRAVEL
- ☐ BOOKS/BOOKSTORE/ LIBRARY
- ☐ GARDENING/PLANTS
- ☐ SPORTS- INDOOR/OUTDOOR
- ☐ BIRD WATCHING
- ☐ RACING
- ☐ ARCHERY
- ☐ EXERCISE/FITNESS

- ☐ VOLUNTEERING
- ☐ PLAY AN INSTRUMENT
- ☐ CRAFTS
- ☐ ART/MUSEUMS
- ☐ PAINTING
- ☐ COLLECTIBLES
- ☐ ENTREPRENUERSHIP
- ☐ MODEL BUILDING
- ☐ CALLIGRAPHY
- ☐ WRITE A BOOK
- ☐ LEARN A NEW LANGUAGE
- ☐ MAGIC
- ☐ PUZZLES/GAMES
- ☐ MARTIAL ARTS

- ☐ SCUBA DIVING
- ☐ TEACH/COACH/ MENTOR
- ☐ ANIMALS
- ☐ HIKING/ ROCK CLIMBING
- ☐ JOURNALING
- ☐ YOGA/PILATES/ BREATHWORK
- ☐ COOK/BAKE
- ☐ KNIT/SEW/ CROCHET
- ☐ VIDEO GAMING
- ☐ FISHING/ BOATING
- ☐ LEARN TO CODE
- ☐ WOOD WORKING
- ☐ MYSTERIES
- ☐ MEDITATION/ MINDFULNESS

OTHER IDEAS:

"The most powerful relationship you will ever have is the relationship with yourself."

~Steve Maraboli

A FEW THINGS ABOUT ME

MY favorite animal:

I would love to travel to:

My favorite school subject is/was:

My favorite genres of music:

How I like to spend my free time:

If I won the lottery I would:

My favorite food:

My favorite movie or TV show:

My favorite childhood memory:

My hero &why:

My happy place:

My biggest pet peeve:

My favorite holiday:

I would like to learn:

What I value most in a friend:

My biggest irrational fear:'

THINGS THAT MAKE ME SMILE

ex. Playing with my dog outside in the yard

ex. Listening to my playlist turned up loud

ex. Looking at old photos on my phone

MY HOBBIES

ex. Vegetable gardening to make my own salsa

ex. Baking and decorating birthday cakes

ex. Thrift store shopping to decorate my apartment

"Learning to love yourself is like learning to walk—essential, life-changing, and the only way to stand tall."

~Vironika Tugaleva

HOBBIES THAT INTEREST ME

ex. Going camping at different state parks

ex. Boxing classes at the gym

ex. Making my own breads and yogurt

MY SELF-CARE PLAYLIST

ex. "Lovely Day", by Bill Wither

ex. "Sunday Best", by Surfaces

ex. "Kind & Generous" by Natalie Merchant

DECLUTTER CHECKLIST

- [ ] Bedroom
- [ ] Bathroom
- [ ] Clothes
- [ ] Kitchen
- [ ] Pantry
- [ ] Garage
- [ ] Basement
- [ ] Attic
- [ ] Storage unit
- [ ] Book collection
- [ ] Kids clothes
- [ ] Sporting equipment
- [ ] Paperwork
- [ ] Email
- [ ] Car
- [ ] Laundry room

"Self-care has become a new priority – the revelation that it's perfectly permissible to listen to your body and do what it needs."

~Frances Ryan

INSTRUMENTS I WANT TO PLAY

ex. Guitar to play around the campfire

ex. Ukulele to play Somewhere Over the Rainbow

ex. Piano to play Christmas carols for the family next year

MOVIES I WANT TO WATCH

ex. Life is Beautiful

ex. Casablanca

ex. Dune

BOOKS I WANT TO READ

ex. The Goldfinch, by Donna Tartt

ex. Beloved, by Toni Morrison

ex. The one I am going to write!

"Take time to do what
makes your soul happy"

~Unknown

PLAYS TO SEE

- [ ] ex. <u>Hamilton</u>, with my kids
- [ ] ex. <u>Wicked</u>, with my mother & my sister
- [ ] ex. <u>Waitress</u>, with friends
- [ ]
- [ ]
- [ ]
- [ ]
- [ ]
- [ ]
- [ ]
- [ ]
- [ ]
- [ ]
- [ ]
- [ ]

TV SHOWS I WANT TO WATCH

ex. Curb Your Enthusiasm

ex. The Office (again and again :)

ex. This is Us

RESTAURANTS I WANT TO TRY

ex. The Ocean House in RI

ex. A restaurant from the food show I watch

ex. Farm to table dinner night at a local farm

"Put yourself at the top of your to-do list every single day and the rest will fall into place."

~Unknown

CONCERTS TO SEE

☐ ex. Foofighters NY this summer ☐

☐ ex. Adele in Boston this Fall ☐

☐ ex. Sam Smith next time he comes this way ☐

☐ ☐

☐ ☐

☐ ☐

☐ ☐

☐ ☐

☐ ☐

☐ ☐

☐ ☐

☐ ☐

☐ ☐

☐ ☐

☐ ☐

CLASSES I WANT TO TAKE

ex. Woodworking to make an adirondack chair

ex. Water color painting at the community center

ex. Speak Itailan before our trip to Italy

PODCASTS I WANT TO LISTEN TO

ex. <u>The Adult Chair</u>, Michelle Chalfant

ex. <u>The Jim Fortin Podcast</u>, Jim Fortin

ex. <u>Creating Confidence</u>, Heather Monahan

"The love and attention you always thought you wanted from someone else, is the love and attention you first need to give to yourself."

~Bryant McGill

TOPICS I WANT TO EXPLORE

ex. DIY home renovations/furniture restoration

ex. Organic gardening/apiaries

ex. Climate change/global warming

PLACES I WANT TO VISIT

ex. Italy, in April with my parents

ex. Hawaii, in October with Ali

ex. The Grand Canyon, in August with my kids

HOW I RECONNECT WITH NATURE

ex. Go for a long drive along the river

ex. Bring fresh flowers into the house

ex. Take a hike in the woods with my dog

"When you can't find your purpose in a day, make it to look after yourself."

~Dodie Clark

WHAT HEALTHY ME LOOKS & FEELS LIKE

ex. Clear, glowing skin

ex. Lots of energy during the day

ex. Feeling comfortable in my clothes

THINGS THAT MAKE MY BODY LOOK & FEEL HEALTHY

ex. Drinking water all-day

ex. Taking at least a 10 minute walk outside every day

ex. Going to bed at 10pm every night

BOOKS THAT HELPED ME HEAL

ex. <u>Codependent No More</u>, by Melody Beattie

ex. <u>Codependency for Dummies</u>, by Darlene Lancer

ex. <u>The Body Keeps Score</u>, by Bessel van der Kolk

"Find what makes your
heart sing and create
your own music."

~Mac Anderson

MY SPIRITUAL PRACTICES

ex. Meditate for 5 minutes every day at noon

ex. Yoga classes at the beach 3x a week

ex. Go to Kirtan once a month

MY BREATHING TECHNIQUES

ex. Breathe in for a count of 5 and out for a count of 5

ex. Breathe in 4, hold 4, out 4, hold 4

ex. Breathe in/out through my nose for 2 minutes

MY FAVORITE MEDITATIONS

ex. Mantra meditation: ex. repeat "I am safe"

ex. Object meditation: focus on an object in the room

ex. Walking meditation: focus on the sensations of my feet

"Your subconscious mind is paying attention to how you treat yourself."

~Sam Owen

PROOF I AM LOVING

ex. I genuinely care about people

ex. The way I raised my children

ex. I connect with strangers easily

PROOF I AM LOVEABLE

ex. My childhood friend knows me well & loves me

ex. Dogs love me

ex. My coworkers love me

I AM PROUD OF MYSELF FOR...

☐ ex. Taking time to rest when I am tired ☐

☐ ex. Saying no to taking on another project at work ☐

☐ ex. Doing the work even when it's hard ☐

☐ ☐

☐ ☐

☐ ☐

☐ ☐

☐ ☐

☐ ☐

☐ ☐

☐ ☐

☐ ☐

☐ ☐

☐ ☐

☐ ☐

"You aren't doing "nothing" when you choose to put your wellbeing first. In fact, this is the key to having everything."

~Brittany Burgunder

PROOF I CAN TRUST MYSELF

ex. I pay my bills on time

ex. I pick the kids up on time

ex. I set boundaries to protect myself

I FORGIVE MYSELF FOR...

ex. Not knowing what I didn't know before I started to heal

ex. Not being there for my kids when they needed me

ex. Using my own addictions to numb myself

MY BOUNDARIES
(FOR MYSELF & OTHERS)

EMOTIONAL:

PHYSICAL:

TIME:

MONEY:

BELONGINGS:

PARENTS:

SIBLINGS:

CHILDREN:

FRIENDS:

RELIGIOUS:

YOUR PAST:

SEXUAL:

TECHNOLOGY/ONLINE:

PRIVACY:

ALCOHOL/DRUGS:

OTHER:

"Practice self-rescue
first before you 'help'
someone else"

~Maureen Joyce Connolly

FAVORITE CHILDHOOD MEMORIES

ex. Swimming in the pool with all of my cousins

ex. Playing school at my house with my friends

ex. Spending time with the family across the street

WHERE I MOST FEEL

SAFE:

LOVED:

ENERGETIC:

PEACEFUL:

CALM:

CONNECTED:

BEAUTIFUL:

MYSELF:

APPRECIATED:

HEALTHY:

SPIRITUAL:

ADVENTUROUS:

INTELLIGENT:

WHOLE:

ALIVE:

CONVERSATIONS I NEED TO HAVE

ex. Boundaries for working when my friends come to visit

ex. A salary increase with my boss

ex. Call my doctor about a concern I have

"It's not selfish to love yourself, take care of yourself, and to make your happiness a priority. It's necessary."

~Mandy Hale

MY IDEAL DAY

ex. Time to take a nap

ex. Time to read a book on my list

ex. Dinner at home with my family

MY IDEAL WEEKEND

ex. Days at the beach kayaking, swimming & reading

ex. Relax by a campfire after dinner

ex. Taking time to work on writing my book

MY IDEAL SPA DAY

- [ ] ex. A hydrating facial
- [ ] ex. A hot stone massage
- [ ] ex. Time to sit and enjoy the relaxation room afterwords
- [ ]
- [ ]
- [ ]
- [ ]
- [ ]
- [ ]
- [ ]
- [ ]
- [ ]
- [ ]
- [ ]

"Be you, love you.
All ways, always."

~Alexandra Elle

MY POLITICAL BELIEFS

I stand for:

I am in involved in:

I would like to be involved in:

MY RELIGIOUS BELIEFS

believe in:

show this through:

would like to:

I WANT MY LEGACY TO BE...

How do you want to be remembered?

"Self-compassion is simply giving the same kindness to ourselves that we would give to others."

~Christopher Germer

RELATIONSHIP GOALS WITH MY...

SELF:

PARENTS:

SIBLINGS:

AT WORK:

FRIENDS:

ROMANTIC PARTNER:

OTHER:

FINANCIAL GOALS

INCOME:

EMERGENCY FUND:

SAVINGS:

INVESTMENTS:

BIG PURCHASES:

HOUSING: RENT/BUY

CHARITABLE GIVING:

OTHER:

MY DREAM HOME IS

ex. On a lake with a beach in South Carolina
_____

ex. Open & inviting to entertain my friends and family
_____

ex. Relaxing and peaceful
_____

_____

_____

_____

_____

_____

_____

_____

_____

_____

_____

_____

_____

_____

"Do something nice for yourself today. Find some quiet, sit in stillness, breathe. Put your problems on pause. You deserve a break."

~Akiroq Brost

MY IDEAL LIFE IN 1 YEAR

ex. I buy my own home

ex. I have peace and stability in my life

ex. I start making & selling jewelry as a side business

MY IDEAL LIFE IN 5 YEARS

ex. My successful side business has replaced my full time job

ex.. My home is in South Carolina

ex. My relationships with my children are strong and healthy

MY IDEAL LIFE IN 10 YEARS

ex. I am healthy and active physically and mentally

ex. I have a full passport

ex. My house is paid off

"Remember that this is YOUR LIFE, and nothing is more important than YOU."

~Miya Yamanouchi

WHAT I NEEDED TO HEAR AS A CHILD

ex. "You are safe"

ex. "What do you need?"

ex. "You are enough."

I AM...

The words you choose to follow this phrase are very important in your healing. Keep these in the present, positive, & what you will replace old negative phrases about yourself.

ex. I am grateful for everything in my life

ex. I am enough at all times

ex. I am confident at work

WHAT TO DO WHEN I HAVE FREE TIME

ex. Call a friend to meet at the beach

ex. Read the books I have waiting for me on my nightstand

ex. Put music on and get my paints out to create something

"Taking care of yourself is the most powerful way to begin to take care of others."

~Bryant McGill

FRIENDS I CAN COUNT ON

ex. Paula. She has kids the same age as I do

ex. My sister helps me remember & understand our childhood

ex. Adriana makes me laugh

MY AFFIRMATIONS

ex. I can set and enforce boundaries to protect myself

ex. I am able to trust myself

ex. I am worthy of love

MY GRATITUDE LIST

ex. I am grateful for the ability to pay my bills

ex. I am grateful for the challenges that have taught me lessons

ex. I am grateful for this day

"An empty lantern provides
no light. Self-care is the
fuel that allows your light
to shine brightly."

~Unknown

"Self-care is not a waste of time. Self-care makes your use of time more sustainable."

~Jackie Viramontez

"When you recover or discover something that nourishes your soul and brings joy, care enough about yourself to make room for it in your life."

~Jean Shinoda Bolen

"You are worth the quiet moment. You are worth the deeper breaths and you are worth the time it takes to slow down, be still, and rest."

~Morgan Harper Nichols

Made in the USA
Coppell, TX
26 February 2022

73896172R00056